THE ONE AND ONLY
Fred

Rupert Fawcett invented Fred seven years ago and both their lives have taken off since then. Rupert has got married and become a father while Fred has become something of a star with books and merchandise in several countries and an animated TV series in the wings. Fred's past life is documented in Rupert's seven previous books, *Fred*, *More Fred*, *The Extraordinary World of Fred*, *The Continued Adventures of Fred*, *Carry on Fred*, *At Home with Fred* and *Pure Fred*. Nowadays Fred can be seen every week in the *Mail on Sunday*.

The One and Only Fred contains sixty-one new illustrations showing Fred in a variety of bizarre situations with the charming Penelope and the faithful black cat, Anthony.

First published in 1997
by HEADLINE BOOK PUBLISHING

10 9 8 7 6 5 4 3 2 1

ISBN 0 7472 7758 3

Printed and bound in Italy by
Canale & C. S.p.A

HEADLINE BOOK PUBLISHING
A division of Hodder Headline PLC
338 Euston Road
London NW1 3BH

THE ONE AND ONLY
Fred

Rupert Fawcett

HEADLINE

FRED AND PENELOPE HAD ALWAYS
SENSED THAT BOB WOULD HAVE
LIKED TO HAVE BEEN MORE
THAN JUST A MILKMAN

IF THE TRUTH BE KNOWN, FRED
WAS SICK TO DEATH OF PENELOPE'S
GARDEN FURNITURE BURGERS

FRED FINALLY FINISHED THE
GRANNY ANNEXE

WHILE PENELOPE SERVED THE
HORS D`OEUVRES, FRED ENTERTAINED
THEIR GUESTS WITH THE STORY OF
HIS IN-GROWING TOE NAIL

AS THEY DEPARTED , FRED'S
GUESTS WERE EACH ISSUED WITH
A COMMEMORATIVE 'T' SHIRT

WHEN FRED AND PENELOPE SET OUT
FOR THEIR MEETING WITH THE LOCAL
PLANNING OFFICER IT WAS WITH
A SENSE OF FOREBODING

PENELOPE KINDLY AGREED TO ASSIST
FRED WITH RESEARCH FOR HIS
FORTHCOMING BOOK, 'A DAY IN THE
LIFE OF A ROLLING PIN'

FRED FOUND THAT BEING
HAUNTED WASN'T ALL BAD

PIP RELUCTANTLY AGREED TO ASSIST
FRED WITH THE TESTING OF HIS
LATEST INVENTION, AN AUTOMATED
NASAL HAIR REMOVER

PENELOPE HAD A TENDENCY TO
MONOPOLISE THE BISCUIT BARREL

FRED TOOK GREAT CARE TO ESTABLISH
THE PRECISE LOCATION OF HIS
MOTHER-IN-LAW'S HOUSE

IMELDA MARCOS HAD
NOTHING ON FRED

WHILE PENELOPE PREPARED THE DINNER
FRED LOOKED AFTER THE DRINKS

FRED COULDN'T HELP FEELING THAT
THE MILKMAN WAS BECOMING A
LITTLE OVER-FAMILIAR

FRED'S GOLF TECHNIQUE OWED A LOT
TO HIS GREAT SPORTING HERO,
ALEX 'HURRICANE' HIGGINS

MR AND MRS NESBIT SENSED THAT
THEY HAD CALLED AT A BAD TIME

ON THE WEEKENDS FRED AND
PIP LIKED TO UNWIND WITH A
FEW GAMES OF PING

IT WAS ONE OF PENELOPE'S
'BAD HAIR' DAYS

FOR A SMALL FEE A FEW HAND-
PICKED INDIVIDUALS WERE ALLOWED
INTO THE HOUSE EACH MORNING
TO WATCH FRED EAT HIS PORRIDGE

OVER THE YEARS PENELOPE GRADUALLY
CAME TO ACCEPT THAT FRED WOULD
NEVER BE A GREAT LOVER

IT WAS EARLY DAYS FOR FRED'S
POLITICAL CAREER

LIFE WITH FRED WAS FULL OF
THE UNEXPECTED

IT GAVE FRED IMMENSE SATISFACTION
TO RECALL PEOPLE'S SCORNFUL
LAUGHTER WHEN HE FIRST
PLANTED THE LIGHT BULB

PENELOPE COULDN'T HELP FEELING
THAT FRED WAS OVER-REACTING
TO THE GREENFLY

MONDAY WAS WASHDAY

FRED WASN'T ENTIRELY HAPPY ABOUT
SHARING THE PANTOMIME HORSE
WITH PENELOPE'S COUSIN FRANK

PENELOPE WAS BECOMING CONCERNED
ABOUT FRED'S DRINKING

FRED AND PENELOPE FELT SURE THAT
BEFORE TOO LONG THE BANK MANAGER
WOULD BEGIN TO SEE THINGS
FROM THEIR POINT OF VIEW

YEARS OF EXPERIENCE HAD TAUGHT
FRED TO PASS NO COMMENT ON
PENELOPE'S KNITTING SKILLS

IT WAS A COMFORT TO PENELOPE AND
FRED TO KNOW THAT IF EVER THEY FELL
UPON HARD TIMES THEY WOULD FETCH
A GOOD PRICE FOR GOD'S SLIPPERS

ONCE AGAIN THE SECRETARY OF THE EXCLUSIVE 'POINTY HAT AND NOSE CLUB' WAS FORCED TO REMIND PIP OF THEIR STRICT DRESS CODE

FRED TOOK ADVANTAGE OF HIS FAMILY'S
CHRISTMAS VISIT TO CARRY OUT SOME
URGENT ROOF REPAIRS

'I BLAME ALL THOSE S.A.S. BOOKS
HE'S BEEN READING', SIGHED PENELOPE

FRED WAS GOING FOR GOLD

HAVING OVERCOME THEIR INITIAL
SHYNESS FRED AND THE CREATURE
FROM THE DEEP FOUND THEY ACTUALLY
HAD QUITE A LOT IN COMMON

PENELOPE WAS DISMAYED TO SEE
FRED FIGHTING WITH THE
NEXT-DOOR NEIGHBOUR AGAIN

FRED AND PENELOPE'S NEW BATHROOM
MIRROR WAS GOING TO TAKE
SOME GETTING USED TO

IT WAS ANOTHER OF FRED'S
MOUNTAINEERING DREAMS

UNFORTUNATELY FOR FRED HIS ESCAPE
TUNNEL CAME UP SIX FEET SHORT
OF THE GARDEN FENCE

WHEN IN PUBLIC PLACES FRED AND
PENELOPE AVOIDED THE UNWELCOME
STARES OF THEIR FANS BY THE
CUNNING USE OF DISGUISE

PENELOPE'S 'IT'S TEDDY OR ME' ULTIMATUM
APPEARED TO HAVE BACKFIRED

FRED HAD NEVER BEEN A GREAT
ONE FOR BIRTHDAY CELEBRATIONS

WHEN THE ABDUCTION WAS OVER ALL
PENELOPE WAS ABLE TO REMEMBER
WAS LOTS OF QUESTIONS ABOUT
OVEREATERS ANONYMOUS

THE TROUBLE WITH HAVING MR AND MRS JIGSAW AROUND WAS THAT ONE OF THEM WOULD ALWAYS LOSE A PIECE

EVEN AS A BOY THE WORLD HAD
SEEMED STRANGE TO FRED

PENELOPE WAS IN THE
MOOD FOR LOVE

FRED FELT IT WAS TIME
FOR A CHANGE

FRED AND PENELOPE'S LITTLE
DISAGREEMENT WAS THE ONLY BLEMISH
ON AN OTHERWISE PERFECT EVENING

PENELOPE'S FRIENDS WISHED
THEY COULD ALL CHANGE THEIR
HUSBANDS HEADS AS EASILY

IT WAS TIME FOR WALKIES

BEING A KEEN GARDENER, FRED
SPENT MANY HAPPY HOURS IN
HIS POTTING SHED

POPPING OVER TO THE NESBITS
FOR TEA AND SCONES WAS NEVER
QUITE AS SIMPLE AS IT SOUNDED

PENELOPE WAS NOT AT ALL
HAPPY WITH FRED'S PENCHANT
FOR VIRTUAL BATHS

FRED AND PENELOPE COULDN'T HELP
NOTICING THAT THE NEIGHBOURHOOD
WAS BECOMING MORE VIOLENT

HAVING VISITED LOURDES AND THE SHROUD
OF TURIN, FRED AND PENELOPE THEN
MADE A PILGRIMAGE TO THE LATEST BIG
ATTRACTION ON THE RELIGIOUS MAP

ABOUT TEN DAYS AFTER FRED'S VISIT
TO THE DOCTOR PENELOPE COULD
SENSE HIS ANTI-DEPRESSANTS
BEGINNING TO KICK IN

CONSIDERING FRED AND PENELOPE HAD
ONLY ATTENDED ONE YOGA CLASS
THEY WERE DOING WELL

PENELOPE WAS SURPRISED THAT :-
A. GOD HAD A WIFE, AND
B. SHE WAS SO VAIN

FRED AND PENELOPE WONDERED WHAT
HAD BECOME OF THEIR GUESTS SINCE THEY
FINISHED THEIR CHRISTMAS DINNER